Deep Trouble: The Hidden Threat of Groundwater Pollution

PAYAL SAMPAT

Jane Peterson, *Editor*

WORLDWATCH PAPER 154

December 2000

THE WORLDWATCH INSTITUTE is an independent, nonprofit environmental research organization in Washington, DC. Its mission is to foster a sustainable society in which human needs are met in ways that do not threaten the health of the natural environment or future generations. To this end, the Institute conducts interdisciplinary research on emerging global issues, the results of which are published and disseminated to decision-makers and the media.

FINANCIAL SUPPORT for the Institute is provided by the Compton Foundation, the Geraldine R. Dodge Foundation, the Ford Foundation, the Richard & Rhoda Goldman Fund, the William and Flora Hewlett Foundation, W. Alton Jones Foundation, Charles Stewart Mott Foundation, the Curtis and Edith Munson Foundation, David and Lucile Packard Foundation, John D. and Catherine T. MacArthur Foundation, Summit Foundation, Turner Foundation, U.N. Population Fund, Wallace Genetic Foundation, Wallace Global Fund, Weeden Foundation, and the Winslow Foundation. The Institute also receives financial support from its Council of Sponsors members—Tom and Cathy Crain, Roger and Vicki Sant, Robert Wallace and Raisa Scriabine, and Eckart Wintzen—and from the many Friends of Worldwatch.

THE WORLDWATCH PAPERS provide in-depth, quantitative and qualitative analysis of the major issues affecting prospects for a sustainable society. The Papers are written by members of the Worldwatch Institute research staff and reviewed by experts in the field. Regularly published in five languages, they have been used as concise and authoritative references by governments, nongovernmental organizations, and educational institutions worldwide.

REPRINT AND COPYRIGHT INFORMATION for one-time academic use of this material is available by contacting Customer Service, Copyright Clearance Center, at (978) 750-8400 (phone), or (978) 750-4744 (fax), or writing to CCC, 222 Rosewood Drive, Danvers, MA 01923. Nonacademic users should call the Worldwatch Institute's Communication Department at (202) 452-1992, x517, or fax a request to (202) 296-7365.

The views expressed are those of the author and do not necessarily represent those of the Worldwatch Institute; of its directors, officers, or staff; or of its funding organizations.

Table of Contents

ACKNOWLEDGMENTS: I am grateful to the following individuals who reviewed this manuscript: Joe Domagalski, Tim Lack, and Adrian Lawrence, who read the entire draft, and Jack Barbash, Wayne Lapham, and Tom Nolan, who commented on specific sections. Stephen Foster and Sandra Postel provided helpful suggestions early on in the process.

Everyone at Worldwatch contributed to this project, and I thank my colleagues for their support. Lester Brown, Gary Gardner, Brian Halweil, Ashley Mattoon, Anne McGinn, intern Mike Montag, and alumnus John Young reviewed preliminary drafts; Ed Ayres edited a magazine article I wrote on the same subject; and Danielle Nierenberg provided outstanding research assistance. I am grateful to several colleagues who pitched in when I most needed help, including Chris Bright, Lori Brown, Jonathan Guzman, Lisa Mastny, Curtis Runyan, David Ruppert, Jennifer Silva, and Christine Stearn. Many thanks to Jane Peterson for her invaluable editorial guidance; to Dick Bell, Niki Clark, and Denise Warden for their outreach efforts; and to Liz Doherty, for her patience and precision while typesetting this Paper.

PAYAL SAMPAT is a Research Associate at Worldwatch Institute, where she writes on freshwater, mining, and materials. She is co-author of Worldwatch Paper 144, *Mind Over Matter: Recasting the Role of Materials in Our Lives*, and of two of the Institute's *State of the World* reports. A native of Bombay, India, she holds degrees from Tufts University in Massachusetts and St. Xavier's College, Bombay.

Introduction

The Mississippi River occupies a mythic place in the American imagination, in part because it is so huge. At any given moment, on average, about 2,100 billion liters of water sweep across Big Muddy's broad bottom. If you were to dive down about 35 feet and lie on that bottom, you might think that the whole river was flowing over you. But in one very important sense, you'd be wrong. At any point in time, only 1 percent of the water in the Mississippi River system is running downstream to the Gulf of Mexico. The other 99 percent lies hidden beneath the bottom, locked in massive strata of rock and sand.[1]

It's natural to think of water as something that flows or evaporates. We see it coming down as rain, coursing in rivers, or drifting around us as fog. But most freshwater is not so easily observed because it lies deep underground in aquifers—geological formations made of porous materials such as sand and gravel, or spaces between subterranean rocks. These formations retain enormous amounts of water. So the Mississippi is not unique in its ratio of surface to underground water: some 97 percent of the planet's liquid freshwater is stored in aquifers.[2]

In the last half-century, as global population and food demand have more than doubled, and rivers and streams have become more polluted, we have increasingly turned to aquifers to supply drinking and irrigation water—and in the process, we have made a sobering discovery. Despite the popular impression that groundwater is shielded from contaminants, scientists are uncovering cases of pollution in aquifers near farms, factories, and cities on every continent. We are now learning that the water buried beneath our feet is not only susceptible to pollution, it is in many ways more vulnerable than water above ground.

This is a distinction of enormous consequence. Because it is underground and slow moving, groundwater stores pollutants far longer than, say, rivers or air do. Hence, the very characteristic that makes aquifers ideal reservoirs of freshwater—their ability to accumulate and retain liquid for longer periods of time—also enables them to become long-term sinks for contaminants. It's true that some aquifers recycle water back to the environment fairly quickly. But the average length of time groundwater remains in an aquifer is 1,400 years, as opposed to just 16 days for river water. Some aquifers contain water that fell as rain as much as 30 millennia ago. So instead of being flushed out to the sea, or becoming diluted with constant additions of freshwater, as rivers, lakes, and streams are, aquifers continue to accumulate pollutants, decade after decade—thus steadily diminishing the amount of clean water they can yield for human use.[3]

Many of the contaminants trickling underground are substances that are routinely used and discarded by modern societies: solvents used to make computer chips, for example, or nitrates from fertilizer applied on cornfields, or chemicals sprayed to kill insects and weeds on plantations and front lawns. Throughout history, civilizations have used the subterranean world as a receptacle for waste—a place to bury the dead, or to landfill trash, for instance. But prior to the twentieth century, these practices did not usually result in serious damage to groundwater. As water percolated down through soil and rocks, bacteria, fungi, and other such biological pollutants were naturally filtered out, or diluted. But in recent years, groundwater's natural defense systems have been vastly overextended. The sheer volume of pollutants sent underground has escalated—and at the same time, scientists have introduced thousands of new substances not found in nature. Globally, the production of synthetic chemicals has vaulted from under 150,000 tons in 1935 to more than 150 million tons in 1995. Many of these substances not only endure far longer in the environment, they are often more toxic than their predecessors. Pesticide formulations available today, for instance, are between 10 and 100 times more potent than those sold in 1975.[4]

Scientists are now learning that the unique makeup of aquifers makes it possible for persistent substances to endure especially long underground. Aquifers usually contain less in the way of minerals, microbes, dissolved oxygen, and organic matter than soils—thus making it difficult for chemicals to break down easily. As a result, the herbicide alachlor, for example, has a half-life—the time it takes for 50 percent of a chemical's mass to decay—of just 20 days in soil, but of nearly four years in groundwater.[5]

Taken together, all these factors—the remoteness of groundwater, its slowness to recharge, the enormous volume of contaminants that reach it, and their slowness to break down underground—make groundwater pollution virtually irreversible. Perhaps the most daunting challenge is the sheer size of many aquifers. The Ogallala, for instance, spans portions of eight states in the midwestern United States, and covers 453,000 square kilometers. The volume of water it would take to purge such a system of chemicals is thus "unimaginably large," notes the U.S. National Research Council. Deeper aquifers are also very hard to get to. And the persistence of many contaminants now found underground further complicates cleanup: some of the radioactive waste that has leaked into an aquifer beneath Washington state, for instance, has a half-life of 250,000 years.[6]

In addition to pollution, the world's groundwater faces a second major onslaught: depletion. Many major aquifers around the world are being drained much more rapidly than their natural rates of recharge, thus shrinking water reserves by an estimated 200 billion cubic meters a year, and effectively spending down precious capital. Removing large amounts of water from an aquifer can magnify the concentration of pollutants in the groundwater that remains. And in some cases, polluted surface flow or salty ocean water may pour into the aquifer to replace the depleted groundwater—thus further shrinking supplies.[7]

Groundwater overuse and pollution have proceeded unchecked in large part because we know so little about the water buried beneath our feet. At present, very few countries have regular monitoring programs to gauge the health of their aquifers. This is partly logistical: it is extremely costly to adequately track the health of underground water resources, for the same reasons that make it so difficult to clean them. The threats to groundwater have thus grown unobtrusively in many places. And where human health is concerned, considerable time can elapse between cause and effect. Even after an underground fuel storage tank begins to leak, for example, it may take several more years before appreciable concentrations of chemicals appear in the aquifer—and it will likely be long after that before any health effects show up in the local population. In Bangladesh, for instance, perhaps half the country's population is now drinking groundwater containing unsafe levels of arsenic, a heavy metal that occurs naturally in Ganges aquifer sediments. But the symptoms of chronic arsenic poisoning can take up to 15 years to surface—and thus no one recognized that the water was toxic until the epidemic was well under way.[8]

By inadvertently poisoning groundwater, we may render what is essentially a renewable resource into one that cannot be recharged or purified within human time scales—and is thus unusable. Fortunately, most groundwater is still of very good quality, but it is unlikely to remain so if current practices continue unchecked. Given the extent of harm chemical pollution can inflict on public health, the environment, and the economy once it gets into the water, it becomes critical that we shift emphasis away from costly end-of-pipe responses to *preventing* the damage in the first place. The United States would have to spend an estimated $1 trillion over the next 30 years even to begin to purify thousands of sites where groundwater pollution is most severe. Yet scientists warn us that this costly process will not be sufficient to undo the damage. At the same time, many practices responsible for the pollution are unnecessary to begin with. The National Research Council estimates that in the United States, between a third and half of nitrogen fertilizer applied to crops cannot be utilized by the plants; much of the excess seeps into water supplies. And roughly 85–90 percent of pesticides used for agriculture never reach target organisms, but instead spread through the air, soil, and water. Streamlining this excess could save millions of dollars now wasted in the unnecessary use—and the consequent mopping up—of chemicals.[9]

Even more radical gains may be within reach by overhauling the polluting systems themselves. In China, for example, by planting more diverse varieties of rice instead of monocultures, thousands of rice farmers have completely eliminated their pesticide use—and at the same time, have doubled their yields. Field-based training has helped farmers in Indonesia, Peru, and Cuba to control pests through nonpolluting biological, rather than chemical, means. Some pioneering water utilities and governments have found that it costs less to support such sustainable farming practices than to strip chemicals out of polluted water. And by reusing discarded materials and spent chemicals, some firms are finding ways to shrink their waste stream—thereby protecting groundwater from chemicals that leak out of landfills and septic systems.[10]

Just as the onset of climate change has awakened us to the fact that the air over our heads is an arena of titanic forces, the water crisis has revealed that slow moving though it may be, groundwater is part of a system of powerful hydrological interactions—between earth, surface water, sky, and sea—that we ignore at our peril. A few years ago, reflecting on how human activity is beginning to affect climate, Columbia University scientist Wallace Broecker warned, "The climate system is an angry beast and we are poking it with sticks." A similar statement might now be made about the system under our feet. If we continue to drill holes into it—expecting it to swallow our waste and yield freshwater in return—we will jeopardize our supplies of the world's most important natural resource in unpredictable ways.[11]

Valuing Groundwater

"...but streams came up from the earth and watered the whole surface at the ground."

— *Genesis 2:6 (Bible, New International Version)*

The ancient Greeks created an elaborate mythology about the Underworld, or Hades, which they described as a dismal, lifeless place lacking the fertility of the world above. But science and human experience have taught us differently. Hydrologists now know that healthy aquifers are essential to life above ground—that they play a vital role not just in providing water to drink, but in replenishing rivers and wetlands and, through their ultimate effects on rainfall and climate, in nurturing the life of the land and air as well. As Henry David Thoreau observed a century and a half ago, "Heaven is under our feet as well as over our heads."

For most of human history, groundwater was tapped mainly in arid regions where surface water was in short supply. Over the centuries, as populations and cropland expanded, water became such a valuable resource that some cultures developed elaborate mythologies imbuing underground water and its seekers with special powers. In medieval Europe, people called water witches or dowsers claimed the ability to detect groundwater using a forked stick and mystical insight.[12]

In the second half of the twentieth century, the soaring demand for water turned the dowsers' modern-day counterparts into a major industry. Today, aquifers are tapped on every continent, and groundwater is the primary source of drinking water for between 1.5 and 2 billion people worldwide. (See Table 1.) The aquifer that lies beneath the Huang-

Huai-Hai plain in eastern China supplies drinking water to nearly 160 million people. Some of the largest cities in the developing world—including Jakarta, Dhaka, Lima, and Mexico City—depend on aquifers for almost all their water. And in rural areas, where centralized supply systems are undeveloped, groundwater is typically the sole source of water. Almost 99 percent of the U.S. rural population and 80 percent of India's depend on groundwater for drinking.[13]

A principal reason for the explosive rise in groundwater use since 1950 has been a dramatic expansion in irrigated agriculture. In India, the leading country in total irrigated area and the world's third largest grain producer, the number of shallow tubewells used to draw groundwater surged from 3,000 in 1950 to 6 million in 1990. Today, aquifers supply water to more than half of India's irrigated land. About 40 percent of India's agricultural output comes from areas irrigated with groundwater, bringing groundwater's contribution to gross domestic product (GDP) to about nine percent. The United States, with the third highest irrigated area in the world, uses groundwater for 43 percent of its irrigated farmland. Worldwide, irrigation is by far the biggest drain on freshwater: it accounts for about two thirds of the water drawn from rivers and wells each year.[14]

While agriculture is the largest groundwater consumer, other sectors of the economy have been expanding their water use even faster—and generating much higher profits in the process. On average, a ton of water used in industry generates roughly $14,000 worth of output—about 70 times as much profit as the same amount of water used to grow grain. Thus, as the world has industrialized, substantial amounts of water have been shifted from farms to more lucrative factories. Industry's share of total consumption has reached 22 percent and is likely to continue rising rapidly. The amount of water available for drinking is thus constrained not only by a limited resource base, but by competition with other, more powerful users.[15]

And as rivers and lakes are stretched to their limits—many of them dammed, dried up, or polluted—people are

TABLE 1

Groundwater as a Share of Drinking Water Use, by Region

Region	Share of Drinking Water from Groundwater	People Served
	(percent)	(million)
Asia-Pacific	32	1,000 to 1,200
Europe	75	200 to 500
Latin America	29	150
United States	51	135
Australia	15	3
Africa	not available	not available
World		1,500 to 2,000

Sources: See endnote 13.

growing more and more dependent on groundwater for all their needs. In Taiwan, for example, the share of water supplied by groundwater almost doubled in just eight years—from 21 percent in 1983 to over 40 percent in 1991. Bangladesh, which was once almost entirely river- and stream-dependent, dug over a million wells in the 1970s to replace its badly polluted surface-water supply. Today, 95 percent of its people use only groundwater for drinking. In wealthier countries, sales of bottled spring water (supposedly from underground sources) are soaring: in the United States, bottled water use grew ninefold between 1978 and 1998.[16]

Even as humanity's dependence on groundwater increases, the availability of the resource is becoming more limited. On almost every continent, many major aquifers are being drained much more rapidly than they are being replenished by nature. Groundwater depletion is most severe in parts of India, China, the United States, North Africa, and the Middle East, resulting in a worldwide water deficit of an estimated 200 billion cubic meters a year. This is roughly equivalent to the amount of water used to grow 10 percent of the global grain harvest each year.[17]

To compound the problem, groundwater overdraft can cause aquifer sediments to compact under certain geological conditions, permanently shrinking the aquifer's storage capacity. This loss can be quite considerable, and is irreversible. The amount of water storage capacity lost because of aquifer compaction in California's Central Valley, for example, is equal to more than 40 percent of the combined storage capacity of all human-made reservoirs across the state. Compacted aquifer sediments can also cause the land above to sink. Such "land subsidence" has occurred in some of the world's most populous places, including Mexico City, Beijing, and some 45 other Chinese cities.[18]

As the competition among factories, farms, and households intensifies, it's easy to overlook the extent to which groundwater is also required for essential ecological services. Groundwater is an important component of the planet's hydrological cycle. When it rains, some of the water trickles into soil and soaks underground into the aquifer. Over centuries, the aquifer gradually releases the water to the surface, and eventually to the sea. Therefore it is not just rainfall, but also groundwater welling up from beneath, that replenishes rivers, lakes, and streams. In a study of 54 streams in different parts of the United States, the U.S. Geological Survey (USGS) found that groundwater is the source for more than half the total flow, on average. The 492 billion gallons (1.86 cubic kilometers) of water that aquifers add to U.S. surface water bodies each day is nearly equal to the daily flow of the Mississippi. Groundwater provides the base contribution for the Mississippi, the Niger, the Yangtze, and many more of the world's great rivers—some of which would otherwise not flow year-round.[19]

Wetlands, important habitat for birds, fish, and other wildlife, are often entirely groundwater fed, created in places where the water table overflows to the surface on a constant basis. Where too much groundwater has been depleted, the result is often dried up riverbeds and desiccated wetlands.

For example, groundwater in Jordan has been overpumped to irrigate fields and supply water to the city of Amman—thus drying out the Azraq, a wetland protected by the Ramsar Convention. The Azraq was once a major destination for migratory birds—and bird-watchers—and when the ecosystem collapsed in the 1980s, so did the local tourist economy.[20]

In addition to providing surface bodies with enough water to keep stable, aquifers also help prevent them from flooding: when it rains heavily, aquifers beneath rivers soak up the excess water, preventing the surface flow from rising too rapidly and overflowing onto neighboring fields and villages. In tropical Asia, where the hot season can last as long as nine months, and where monsoon rains can be very intense, this dual hydrological service is of critical value. Aquifers also provide a way to store freshwater without losing much liquid to evaporation—another service that is especially valuable in hot, drought-prone regions, where such losses can be quite high. In Africa, for instance, on average a third of the water removed from reservoirs each year is lost via evaporation.[21]

Tracking the Hidden Crisis

In 1940, during the Second World War, the U.S. Department of the Army acquired 70 square kilometers of land around Weldon Spring and its neighboring towns near St. Louis, Missouri. Where farmhouses and barns had once stood, the Army established the world's largest TNT-producing facility. In this sprawling warren of plants, toluene (a component of gasoline) was treated with nitric acid to produce more than a million tons of the explosive compound each day at the peak of production.[22]

Part of the manufacturing process involved purifying the TNT—washing off unwanted "nitroaromatic" compounds left behind by the chemical reaction between the toluene and nitric acid. Over the years, millions of gallons of this reddish muck were generated. Some of it was treated at wastewater plants, but much of it ran off from the leaky treatment facilities into ditches and ravines and soaked into the ground. In 1945, when the Army left the site, soldiers burned down the contaminated buildings but left the red-tinged soil and the rest of the area as they were. For decades, the site remained abandoned and unused.[23]

Then, in 1980, the U.S. Congress passed its "Superfund" legislation, which required the cleaning up of several sites that were contaminated with hazardous waste. Weldon Spring made it to the list of sites that were the highest priority for cleanup. The Army Corps of Engineers was assigned the task, and what the Corps workers found baffled them. While they expected the soil and vegetation around the site to be contaminated with the nitroaromatic wastes that had been discarded there, they found that the chemicals were also showing up in people's wells in towns several miles from the site. No one had anticipated this turn of events because the original pollution had been completely localized. Eventually, geologists determined that there was an enormous plume of contamination in the water below the TNT factory, and that it had worked its way through fissures in the limestone rock to other parts of the aquifer over the previous 35 years.[24]

The Weldon Spring story may sound like an exceptional case of clumsy planning combined with a particularly vulnerable geological structure. But in fact there is nothing exceptional about it at all. Across the United States, as well as in parts of Europe, Asia, and Latin America, human activities are still unwittingly sending dangerous chemicals and pollutants into groundwater. In some cases, the pollution originates from specific, or "point" sources—landfills, septic systems, or storage tanks that leak gasoline or other chemicals. Such contamination is typically localized, but can be very intense. Far more diffuse—but much harder to control—are the "non-point" sources of pollution: nitrates running off from poultry farms and golf courses into waterways, or pesticides sprayed over hundreds of acres of orchards.

The unforeseen turn of events at Weldon Spring shows that we cannot always anticipate where the pollution is going to turn up in our water—or how long it will be from the time it was deposited until it reappears. Because it can often take months or years for a chemical to make its way from the surface into groundwater, damage done to aquifers may not show up for decades. In many parts of the world, scientists are only beginning to discover contamination caused by practices of 30 or 40 years ago. Some of the most egregious cases of aquifer contamination now being unearthed date back to Cold War era nuclear weapons-making and testing.

As this covert crisis unfolds, we are only beginning to understand its dimensions. Even hydrogeologists and health officials have only a hazy impression of the likely extent of groundwater damage in different parts of the world. Few countries track the health of their aquifers—their enormous size and remoteness make them extremely expensive to monitor. Nonetheless, given the data we now have, it is possible to sketch a rough map of the regions affected and the principal threats they face. (See Table 2.)[25]

Jack Barbash, an environmental chemist at the U.S. Geological Survey, points out that it may not be necessary to wait for expensive tests to alert us to what to expect in our groundwater. "If you want to know what you're likely to find in aquifers near Shanghai or Calcutta, just look at what's used above ground," he says. "If you've been applying DDT to a field for 20 years, for example, that's one of the chemicals you're likely to find in the underlying groundwater." While the full consequences of today's chemical-dependent and waste-producing economies may not become apparent for another generation, Barbash and other scientists are beginning to get a sense of just how serious those consequences are likely to be if present consumption and disposal practices continue.[26]

TABLE 2

Some Major Threats to Groundwater

Threat	Sources	Health and Ecosystem Effects at High Concentrations	Principal Regions at Risk
Nitrates	Fertilizer runoff; manure from livestock operations; septic systems	Suffocation and death in infants; digestive tract and other cancers. Algal blooms and eutrophication in surface water	Parts of midwestern and mid-Atlantic United States, North China Plain, Northern India, Eastern Europe
Pesticides	Runoff from farms, backyards, golf courses; landfill leaks	Some linked to reproductive and endocrine disorders; nervous system damage and cancers	Parts of United States, China, India
Petro-Chemicals	Underground petroleum storage tanks	Benzene and other petrochemicals can cause cancer even at low exposure	United States, United Kingdom, parts of former Soviet Union
Chlorinated solvents	Effluents from metals and plastics degreasing; fabric cleaning; electronics and aircraft manufacture	Linked to reproductive disorders and some cancers	California state in United States, industrial zones in East Asia
Arsenic	Naturally occurring	Nervous system and liver damage; skin cancers	Bangladesh, West Bengal, India, Nepal, Taiwan
Radioactive materials	Nuclear testing and medical waste	Increased risk of certain cancers	Western United States, parts of former Soviet Union
Fluoride	Naturally occurring	Dental problems; crippling spinal and bone damage	Northern China, Northwestern India, Sri Lanka, Thailand, and East Africa
Salts	Seawater intrusion	Freshwater unusable for drinking or irrigation	Coastal China and India, Gulf coasts of Mexico and Florida, Australia

Sources: See endnote 25.

Nitrates: From Green Revolution to "Blue Baby"

"The water of the garden
Will run off underground
So that thou wilt never
Be able to find it."

— *The Koran, Sura 18:41*[27]

A lot has changed in the centuries since these early groundwater observations were written. For one, we've developed ingenious ways to locate and tap the hidden water. And in the last century, the water of "the garden"—and of the millions of acres of global crop- and pastureland—carries with it chemicals that were never intended to "run off underground." Fertilizers and pesticides applied to cropland are the leading sources of chemical pollution of groundwater in farming regions around the world.

Since the early 1950s, farmers have stepped up their use of nitrogen fertilizers 20-fold in an attempt to boost yields. But the larger doses of nutrients often cannot be fully utilized by plants. A study conducted over a 140,000 square kilometer region of Northern China, for example, found that crops used on average only 40 percent of the nitrogen that was applied. The U.S. National Research Council estimates that in the United States, between a third and half of nitrogen fertilizer applied to plants is wasted. In an aerobic (oxygen-containing) environment, nitrogen is converted to nitrate—a form more readily used by plants. Much of the unused nitrate dissolves in rain and irrigation water, eventually trickling through the soil into underlying aquifers.[28]

Joining the excess chemical fertilizer from farm crops is the organic waste generated by farm animals and the sewage produced by cities—both of which have high nitrate content. Livestock waste forms a particularly potent tributary to the stream of excess nutrients flowing into the environment, because of its enormous volume. In the United States, farm animals produce 130 times as much waste as the country's people do—with the result that millions of tons of cow and pig feces are washed into streams and rivers, or seep into groundwater. To this Augean burden can be added the innumerable leaks and overflows from urban sewage systems, the fertilizer runoff from suburban lawns, golf courses, and landscaping, and the nitrates leaking (along with other pollutants) from landfills.[29]

Nitrate pollution of groundwater has become particularly severe in places where human population—and the demand for high food productivity—is most concentrated. In the northern Chinese counties of Beijing, Tianjin, Hebei, and Shandong, nitrate concentrations in groundwater exceeded 50 milligrams per liter (mg/liter) in more than half of the locations studied. (The World Health Organization [WHO] drinking water guideline is 45 mg/liter of nitrate.) In some places, the concentration had risen as high as 300 mg/liter. It is likely that these levels have increased, as fertilizer applications have escalated since the tests were carried out in 1995. They may increase even more as China's population (and demand for food) swells, and as more farmland is lost to urbanization, industrial development, nutrient depletion, and erosion.[30]

Reports from other regions show similar results. (See Table 3.) In India's breadbasket states of Punjab and Haryana, where nitrogen fertilizer is applied intensively, wells tested in the early 1990s contained nitrate at levels five to 15 times higher than the safe limit. The USGS found that about 15 percent of shallow groundwater sampled below agricultural and urban areas in the United States in the mid-1990s had nitrate concentrations higher than the guideline; in some states, such as Nebraska, more than a third of all wells exceeded this limit. In Sri Lanka's Jaffna Peninsula, 79 percent of wells sampled by the British Geological Survey had nitrate levels above the guideline. And the European Topic Centre on Inland Waters found that in Romania and Moldova, more than 35 percent of the sites sampled in the mid-1990s had nitrate concentrations higher than 50 mg/liter.[31]

Although there is little historical information available about trends in the pollution of aquifers, several studies indicate that nitrate concentrations have increased as fertilizer applications and population size have grown. In California's

TABLE 3

High Nitrate Levels in Groundwater, Selected Regions, 1990s[1]

Region	Nitrate Levels	Sources
Northern China	Above 50 mg/liter in more than half the locations tested	Fertilizer runoff from farms
Yogyakarta, Indonesia	Above 50 mg/liter in half the wells tested	Septic tanks
Canary Islands	Ranged between 70 and 265 mg/liter in wells beneath banana plantations	High nitrogen fertilizer use on banana plantations
Central Nigeria	Ranged between 50 and 500 mg/liter in wells tested near small towns	Human and animal waste disposal
Romania	Above 50 mg/liter in 35 percent of groundwater tested	Unsewered wastewater
East Anglia, United Kingdom	Above 50 mg/liter in 142 locations tested	Fertilizer leaching from fields
Yucatán Peninsula, Mexico	Shallow groundwater had levels above 45 mg/liter at more than half the locations tested	Domestic animal and human waste; agricultural runoff
Nebraska and Kansas, United States	Above 45 mg/liter in 35 percent of samples tested	Fertilizer runoff from farms

[1]Levels found exceeded the WHO drinking water limit of 45 mg of nitrate per liter.
Sources: See endnote 31.

Central Valley, for instance, nitrate levels in groundwater increased 2.5 times between the 1950s and 1980s—a period in which fertilizer inputs grew sixfold. Levels in Danish groundwater have nearly tripled since the 1940s.[32]

What happens when nitrates get into drinking water? Consumed in high concentrations—at levels above 45 mg/liter—they can cause infant methemoglobinemia, or so-called blue-baby syndrome. Because of their low gastric acidity, infant digestive systems convert nitrate to nitrite, which blocks the oxygen-carrying capacity of a baby's blood, causing suffocation and death. Since 1945, about 3,000 cases have been reported worldwide—nearly half of them in Hungary, where private wells have particularly high concentrations of nitrates. Ruminant livestock such as goats, sheep, and cows are vulnerable to methemoglobinemia in much the same way infants are because their digestive systems also quickly convert nitrate to nitrite. Nitrates have been linked to miscarriages in women and to an increased risk of non-Hodgkin's lymphoma. They have also been implicated in digestive tract cancers, although the epidemiological link is still uncertain.[33]

In cropland, nitrate pollution of groundwater can have a paradoxical effect. When nitrate-laden water is used to irrigate crops, the net result may be to reduce rather than to increase production. Yields are often substantially lower: in Libya, for example, grapevines irrigated with water containing 50 mg/liter of nitrogen bore almost no fruit. Too much nitrate can also weaken plants' immune systems, making them more vulnerable to pests and disease. Over-fertilizing makes wheat more susceptible to wheat rust, for example, and it makes pear trees more vulnerable to fire blight. At concentrations above 30 mg/liter, but sometimes as low as 5 mg/liter, nitrate applications can delay crop maturity, severely damage plant roots, and thin stems and branches, making it difficult for plants to bear their own weight. The U.N. Food and Agriculture Organization (FAO) reports that in general, too much nitrogen in irrigation water has the same effect on crops as using too much fertilizer.[34]

Nitrates in groundwater can also damage surface ecosystems. Consider the case of the Chesapeake Bay in the mid-Atlantic United States. Once a thriving ecosystem and vibrant fishery, much of the bay is now suffering the consequences of too many nutrients. Enormous volumes of nitrogen and phosphorus are washed into its waters each day from the region's chicken farms, cropland, and septic systems; these nutrients spur the growth of algae, which now cover the water's surface. Massive algal blooms slowly atrophy the ecosystem by blocking sunlight from sea grasses, which provide important habitat for fish and shellfish, and food for waterfowl. And when the algae die, their decomposition sucks up dissolved oxygen, killing off other aquatic species.[35]

The Bay's plight has alarmed many of the region's residents, but what might not be as apparent is groundwater's role in the ecosystem's collapse. Almost half of the nutrients that pour into the Bay are carried there by aquifers, either directly or, more typically, via the region's streams: groundwater contributes more than half of the 190 billion liters of water that rivers and streams empty into the Chesapeake Bay every day. This is true for nitrates in surface water elsewhere too: researchers found that almost half of the nitrate in Wisconsin's Lake Mendota, for instance, came from groundwater infusions.[36]

The amount of a chemical that reaches groundwater depends on a number of factors: the amount used above ground, the geology of the region, climate, cropping practices, and the characteristics of the chemical itself, such as how mobile and soluble it is in water. Aquifers that are fractured in many places, and that lie below coarse-textured and porous soils, can be very vulnerable to pollution. This is true for the basalt and the sand and gravel deposits that lie beneath southeastern Washington state's potato and corn fields. These row crops are heavily irrigated, thus expediting the flow of water and chemicals into the underlying aquifer. Another reason irrigation is often linked to higher levels of groundwater nitrate is that, in general, more nitrogen fertilizer is applied to irrigated fields than to non-irrigated ones. Other aquifers may be less susceptible: the relatively impermeable clay soils in some parts of the U.S. Midwest, for example, make it difficult for water and chemicals to seep underground. Because the soils drain water so poorly, the region's farmers have constructed tile drains and ditches to divert the excess irrigation water. As a result, farm chemicals run off over land into streams and lakes, which is why the region's surface water has among the highest nitrate levels in the country.[37]

Almost half of the nutrients that pour into the [Chesapeake] Bay are carried there by aquifers.

In places where farms are adjacent to woods and forests, groundwater nitrate levels are often significantly lower. This is because forested areas create conditions that prevent the biological transformation of nitrogen into nitrate. Vegetation can also act as a filter, absorbing some of the nutrients before they enter groundwater. And the nutrient-rich water from farms may be diluted by water recharged into the aquifer by forests. This occurs in the southeastern U.S. states of Georgia and Florida, where the ratio of woodland to cropland is relatively high—and where groundwater nitrate concentrations are low, on average. Even in the nutrient-laden Chesapeake Bay watershed, the lowest levels of nitrate in groundwater were reported in areas where farms were interspersed with woodland. On the other hand, groundwater beneath homogeneous farmland is more likely to carry high levels of nitrate.[38]

Some farming practices can have very long-lasting effects, as in the case of Runnels County, Texas. Here, nitrate levels averaged 250 mg/liter in the early 1970s—and reached 3,100 mg/liter in some wells—even though very little fertilizer was used in the area at the time. The original source of the chemical is thought to be naturally occurring soil nitrogen, which was converted to nitrate by the extensive plowing of grassland in the early 1900s. Since plowing aerates the soil, it creates ideal, oxygen rich conditions for nitrate formation; it also uncovers the protective upper layers of soil, leaving lower reaches vulnerable to pollution.[39]

Pesticides on Tap

Pesticides are designed to kill. Yet it took several years after the first synthetic pesticides were introduced in the 1940s before it became apparent that these chemicals were also injuring organisms other than pests—including humans. Even after the health threats of some of these poisons were widely recognized in the 1960s, scientists believed that the real dangers lay in their dispersal among animals and plants—not deep underground. It was generally assumed that very little pesticide would leach below the upper layers of soil, and that if it did, it would be degraded before it could get any deeper. Soil, after all, is known to be a natural filter, purifying water as it trickles through. Industrial or agricultural chemicals, like such natural contaminants as bacteria or leaf mold, would be filtered out as the water percolated through the soil, or so it was thought.[40]

But over the past 35 years, this seemingly safe assumption has proved mistaken. Cases of pesticide contamination of groundwater have come to light in farming regions of the United States, Western Europe, and South Asia. In the United States, for instance, nearly 60 percent of wells sampled in agricultural areas contained some level of these chemical compounds. And because they are also used to get rid of weeds on front lawns and golf courses, and to kill mosquitoes and other disease-carrying insects, pesticides also lurk in aquifers below cities and suburbs.[41]

We now know that pesticides not only leach into aquifers, but sometimes remain there long after the chemical is no longer used. The organochlorine pesticide DDT, for instance, is still found in U.S. groundwater even though its use was banned 30 years ago. In the San Joaquin Valley of California, the soil fumigant DBCP (dibromochloropropane), which was used intensively in fruit orchards before it was banned in 1977, still lingers in the region's water supplies. Of 4,507 wells sampled by the USGS between 1971 and 1988, nearly a third had DBCP levels that were at least 10 times higher than the maximum allowed by drinking water standards. And dieldrin, an organochlorine that was used for termite control around metropolitan Atlanta until its use was prohibited in 1987, showed up in the city's well water in tests conducted in the mid-1990s.[42]

In places where organochlorines are still widely used, the risks continue to mount. After half a century of spraying in the eastern Indian states of West Bengal and Bihar, for example, the Central Pollution Control Board found DDT in groundwater at levels as high as 4,500 micrograms per liter—several *thousand* times higher than what is considered acceptable. Organochlorines are especially dangerous because they accumulate in body fat and tissue, and because their concentration magnifies as they move up the food chain.[43]

In recent decades, chemical companies have developed hundreds of compounds that are highly toxic, but considered less ecologically damaging because they are short-lived. A pesticide's persistence is measured in terms of its half-life in soil. What scientists are learning to their chagrin, however, is that pesticides are far more persistent in groundwater than they are in soil. The herbicide alachlor, for instance, has a half-life of 20 days in soil, but of nearly four years in groundwater. This is because conditions in aquifers, especially in the deeper reaches, make it harder for pesticides to break down, as they might in soil. Aquifers typically contain less dissolved oxygen, minerals, and organic matter than soils, and fewer microbes that can help break down chemicals.[44]

Many of the pesticides that have replaced the organochlorines are known to be acutely toxic to humans and wildlife. The organophosphate and carbamate insecticides, for instance, are neurotoxins, or nerve poisons. A number of herbicides frequently detected in groundwater—including alachlor, atrazine, and triazine—are thought to interfere with the body's reproductive systems. And several pesticides are known to cause cancers, suppress the body's immune systems, or interfere with childhood development.[45]

Pesticides are often found in combination, because most farms use a range of toxins to destroy different kinds of insects, weeds, and plant diseases. The USGS detected two or more pesticides in groundwater at nearly a quarter of the sites sampled across the United States. (See Table 4.) In the Central Columbia Plateau aquifer, which lies under the states of Washington and Idaho, two thirds of water samples contained multiple pesticides. And even when the original pesticide does not appear to be in groundwater, its breakdown components, or degradates, often show up. When USGS researchers tested for this phenomenon, degradates of herbicides turned up more frequently in groundwater than the original, or parent, compounds. For example, although just 1 percent of wells sampled in Iowa contained alachlor at levels above 0.2 micrograms per liter, more than half contained

TABLE 4

Groundwater Contamination in the United States, Selected Chemicals, 1990s

Chemical Group	Share of Groundwater		
	Containing at least one chemical in group	Containing two or more chemicals in group	Above drinking water guidelines for a single chemical
	(percent)		
Nitrates	71	not applicable[1]	15
Pesticides	50	25	not significant
Volatile Organic Compounds[2]	47[3]	29	6

[1]However, nitrates are typically found in aquifers where pesticides are detected.   [2]A small share of these VOCs are used as pesticides.
[3]Samples from urban areas only.
Sources: See endnote 46.

its degradates. (See Figure 1.) These compounds can be as persistent and toxic as the original pesticide, or more so.[46]

Scientists are not entirely sure what happens when these chemicals come together. Water quality standards do not exist for the many hundred *individual* pesticides in use—the U.S. Environmental Protection Agency (EPA) has drinking water standards for just 33 of these compounds—to say nothing of the infinite variety of toxic blends now trickling into the groundwater. But a recent study provides some indication of possible additive or synergistic surprises we can expect. When researchers at the University of Wisconsin examined the effects of aldicarb, atrazine, and nitrate blends in groundwater—a mixture typically found beneath U.S. farms—they found that "more biological responses occur in the presence of mixtures of common groundwater contaminants than if contaminants occur singly." Fluctuation in concentrations of the thyroid hormone, for example, is a typical response to mixtures, but not usually to individual chemicals. Other research found that combinations of pesticides increased the incidence of fetal abnormalities in the children of pesticide sprayers.[47]

While the most direct impacts may be on the water we drink, there is also concern about what occurs when the pesticide-laden water below farmland is pumped back up for irrigation. One apparent consequence is a reduction in crop yields. In 1990, the now-defunct U.S. Office of Technology Assessment reported that herbicides in shallow groundwater had the effect of "pruning" crop roots, thereby retarding plant growth.[48]

And because groundwater interacts with surface water, its pesticide content threatens aquatic life too. For instance, groundwater is the principal source of pesticides entering the Cedar River in Iowa. When streams and rivers feed aquifers during the rainy season, the reverse is often true. In the U.S. Corn Belt, wells located near streams—and therefore recharged by them—were twice as likely to contain herbicides as those further away.[49]

Heavy spraying has had another unexpected outcome:

FIGURE 1

Herbicides In Groundwater, Iowa, United States, 1996

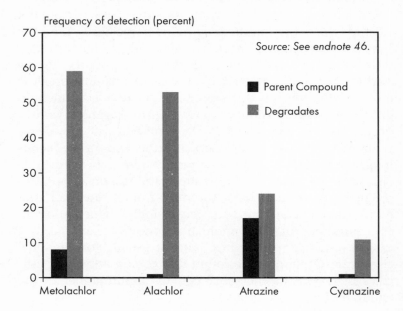

Frequency of detection (percent)

Source: See endnote 46.

■ Parent Compound
■ Degradates

Metolachlor   Alachlor   Atrazine   Cyanazine

nearly 1,000 species of insects, microbes, and weeds have evolved resistance to the pesticides meant to kill them. Thus, although farmers use more chemicals than ever before, crop losses are still as high, or greater, than they were 50 years ago. In the United States, for example, while pesticide use grew 10-fold between the 1940s and the 1990s, the share of crops that farmers lost to pests climbed from 30 to 37 percent.[50]

Although most studies on pesticide contamination have been conducted in temperate regions, these chemicals pose serious risks to groundwater in the tropics as well. Researchers found such extensive atrazine contamination beneath sugarcane plantations in Barbados that they concluded the chemical was "more or less ubiquitous" in the island's coral limestone aquifer. (Barbados' residents get almost all their water from this aquifer.) And unsafe levels of the soil insecticide carbofuran and its more persistent degradate carbofuran-phenol were detected in groundwater under vegetable farms on Sri Lanka's northwest coast, where soils are sandy and permeable.[51]

VOCs: From Tank of Gas to Drinking Glass

San Jose, California, is the capital of the world's high-tech industry. As you drive into the city, it may be hard to imagine that the squeaky-clean veneer of the computer industry conceals a dirty underbelly: Silicon Valley has more Superfund sites than any other area its size in the United States. Its pollution is reflected not in smokestacks, but underground, in contaminated aquifers beneath the valley. The source? Thousands of underground tanks that leak chlorinated solvents and other chemicals that are either stored or discarded by Silicon Valley's assorted electronics industries. In industrial countries, waste that is too hazardous to landfill is routinely buried in underground tanks. But as these caskets age, they eventually spring leaks. As of February 2000, there were about 386,000 confirmed leaks from underground storage tanks in the United States. In Silicon Valley, local groundwater authorities found that 85 percent of the tanks they inspected had holes.[52]

Pull into any gas station in the United States, and you are likely to park over a second pervasive groundwater threat: an underground storage tank for petroleum. Like the tanks that store solvents, many of them were installed two or three decades ago. Left in place long past their expected lifetimes, many have rusted through in places—allowing a steady trickle of chemicals into the ground. EPA estimates that in the United States, about 100,000 of these tanks are leaking. In 1993, petroleum giant Shell reported that a third of its 1,100 gas stations in the United Kingdom were known to have contaminated soil and groundwater. Because the tanks are underground, they are expensive to dig up and repair, so the leakage in some cases continues for years. Petroleum and its associated chemicals—benzene, toluene, and gasoline additives such as MTBE, a fuel oxygenate added to reduce carbon monoxide emissions—constitute the most common category of groundwater contaminant found in aquifers in the United States.[53]

Both petrochemicals and chlorinated solvents are types of synthetic chemicals known as volatile organic compounds, or VOCs, whose chemical and physical properties allow them to move freely between water and air. VOCs often turn up in groundwater beneath industrial areas and cities: they were detected in almost half the wells sampled near U.S. cities between 1985 and 1995. Between 35 million and 50 million people in these urban areas may be drinking water containing varying levels of these compounds.[54]

One reason for their ubiquity is that these compounds are very widely used—they are contained in paints, adhesives, gasoline, plastics, and hundreds of other everyday products. They are also used for cleaning and degreasing in the electronics and aerospace industries and by small firms such as photo developers and dry cleaners.[55]

"In hindsight, it is hardly surprising that solvents would cause groundwater pollution," according to James Pankow and John Cherry, leading scientists studying the incidence of these chemicals in groundwater. The physical and chemical makeup of the compounds is largely to blame. They do not stick to soils, meaning that almost none of the chemical is absorbed by sediments on its underground journey. Because many solvents are denser than water, they can sink deep into an aquifer. And since many do not degrade easily, they can remain there for a very long time, dissolving slowly and circulating to other parts of the aquifer—as happened in Weldon Spring.[56]

VOCs can be dangerous to human and animal health when they are consumed even in tiny concentrations. Petrochemicals such as benzene, for example, are cancer-causing at extremely low levels. Women exposed to chlorinated solvents have a two- to fourfold higher incidence of miscarriages. These compounds have also been linked to kidney and liver damage and childhood cancers. An early case came from the town of Woburn, Massachusetts, in the 1970s, where a cluster of childhood leukemia cases was traced back to high levels of the chlorinated solvents perchloroethylene (PERC) and trichloroethylene (TCE) in the city's wells.[57]

Ironically, a major factor in such contamination is that in most places people have learned to dispose of waste—to remove it from sight and smell—so effectively that it is easy to forget that Earth is a closed ecological system in which nothing permanently disappears. The methods normally used to conceal garbage and other waste—landfills, septic tanks, and sewers—become the major conduits of chemical pollution of groundwater. In the United States, businesses drain almost 2 million kilograms of assorted chemicals into septic systems each year, contaminating the drinking water of 1.3 million people. In many parts of the developing world, factories still dump their liquid effluent onto the ground and wait for it to disappear. In part, it's because these compounds are volatile—as their name suggests—that it has seemed deceptively easy to get rid of them. When poured over the earth, as they were in Woburn, VOCs seem to disappear completely, to evaporate into the atmosphere. But inevitably, some amount seeps underground and gets into groundwater. And even protected landfills can be a potent source of aquifer pollution: in 1995, EPA found that a quarter of the landfills in the U.S. state of Maine, for example, had contaminated groundwater.[58]

Sometimes waste is funneled directly into aquifers. Sixty percent of the most hazardous liquid waste in the United States—34 billion liters of solvents, heavy metals, and radioactive materials—is injected straight into deep groundwater via thousands of "injection wells" across the country. Although EPA requires that these effluents be injected below

> **Earth is a closed ecological system in which nothing permanently disappears.**

the deepest source of drinking water, some have entered aquifers used for water supplies in parts of Florida, Texas, Ohio, and Oklahoma. And in India, a study across five industrializing states—Gujarat, Haryana, Punjab, Andhra Pradesh, and Karnataka—found that scores of factories were illegally injecting their wastes into tubewells that were used to pump out drinking and irrigation water.[59]

Like pesticides, VOCs are typically found in combination. In the United States, 29 percent of wells tested near urban areas contained multiple VOCs (see Table 4); overall, a total of 46 different kinds of these compounds turned up in groundwater. But Paul Squillace, the lead researcher in the study notes that "because current health criteria are based on exposure to a single contaminant, the health implications of these mixtures are not known."[60]

VOCs have been detected in groundwater in other industrialized countries as well. In the Netherlands, one study found that 28 percent of groundwater used for drinking contained PERC, a solvent used widely in dry cleaning, at levels greater than 10 micrograms per liter. Chlorinated solvents were found in close to half the groundwater used for drinking in England in 1985. And a survey of 15 Japanese cities found that 30 percent of all groundwater supplies contained varying levels of chlorinated solvents, although just 3 percent were above prescribed limits. The source was leaky storage tanks from electronics industries. Few data are available from other rapidly industrializing countries of East Asia, but this is a region where VOC use is accelerating. For instance, the production of semiconductor chips, which involves chlorinated solvents, is expected to nearly triple in the Asia-Pacific region (excluding Japan) between 1999 and 2003.[61]

Some of the greatest shocks may be felt in places where chemical use and disposal have climbed in the last few decades, but where the most basic measures to shield groundwater have not been taken. In India, for example, the Central Pollution Control Board surveyed 22 major industrial zones and found that groundwater in every one of them was unfit for drinking. When asked about these findings, the Board's chairman D.K. Biswas remarked, "The result is frightening, and it is my belief that we will get more shocks in the future."[62]

The Threat of Natural Contaminants

"Water takes on the properties of the rocks through which it has passed."
                                    — Pliny[63]

In the early 1990s, several villagers living near India's West Bengal border with Bangladesh began to complain of skin sores that wouldn't heal. A researcher at Calcutta's Jadavpur University, Dipanker Chakraborti, recognized the lesions immediately as early symptoms of chronic arsenic poisoning. In later stages, the disease can lead to gangrene, skin cancer, damage to vital organs, and eventually, death. In the months that followed, Chakraborti began to get letters from doctors and hospitals in Bangladesh, who were seeing streams of patients with similar symptoms. By 1995, it was clear that the region faced a crisis of untold proportions, and that the source of the poisoning was water from tubewells, from which 95 percent of Bangladesh gets its drinking water.[64]

Experts estimate that today, arsenic in drinking water could threaten the health of between 20 and 75 million Bangladeshis—more than half the country's population—and another 6 to 30 million people in West Bengal, India. As many as 1 million wells in the region may be contaminated with the heavy metal at levels between 5 and 100 times the WHO drinking water guideline of 0.01 mg/liter. Arsenic poisoning has already caused at least 7,000 deaths, say local officials in Bangladesh. WHO predicts that within a few years, one in 10 deaths in southern Bangladesh may be from arsenic-related cancers.[65]

How did the arsenic get into groundwater? Until the early 1970s, rivers and ponds supplied most of Bangladesh's drinking water. Concerned about the risks of waterborne disease, international aid agencies launched a well-drilling program to tap groundwater instead. However, the agencies, unaware that soils of the Ganges aquifers are naturally rich in arsenic, did not test the sediment before drilling tubewells. Because the effects of chronic arsenic poisoning can take up to 15 years to appear, the epidemic was not recognized until it was well under way.[66]

One in 10 deaths in southern Bangladesh may be from arsenic-related cancers.

Scientists are still debating what chemical reactions released the arsenic from the mineral matrix in which it is naturally bound up. Some theories implicate human activities. One hypothesis is that as large quantities of water were pumped out of the wells, atmospheric oxygen entered the aquifer, oxidizing the pyrite sediments, and causing the arsenic to dissolve. Another points to the role of iron-rich minerals that contain arsenic, which are common in the alluvial sediments of the aquifer. This theory proposes the reverse of the previous one: arsenic is released when the minerals come into contact with groundwater that lacks oxygen. An October 1999 article in the scientific journal *Nature* by geologists from the Indian Institute of Technology suggests that phosphates from fertilizer runoff and decaying organic matter may have played a role. The nutrient might have spurred the growth of soil microorganisms, which helped to loosen arsenic from sediments.[67]

Salt is another naturally occurring groundwater pollutant that is often introduced by human activity. Normally, water in coastal aquifers empties into the sea. But when too much is pumped out of these aquifers, the process is reversed: seawater moves inland and enters the aquifer. Because of its high salt content, just 2 percent of seawater mixed with freshwater makes the water unusable for drinking or irrigation. And once salinized, a freshwater aquifer can remain contaminated for a very long time. Brackish aquifers frequently have to be abandoned because desalinization is very expensive. This has been the case in Bangkok, Thailand,

and in Madras, India. In the district of Saurashtra in India's western state of Gujarat, for instance, groundwater is so heavily overpumped that seawater has traveled inland as much as 7 kilometers. This has led to the collapse of the local farm economy, which was dependent on the groundwater. Dozens of villages along this coast have to abandon their homes and move inland each year, because of salt water in their aquifers.[68]

Similarly, in Manila, where groundwater levels have fallen 50–80 meters because of overdraft, seawater has flowed as far as 5 kilometers into the Guadalupe aquifer that lies below the city. Salt water has traveled several kilometers inland into aquifers beneath Jakarta in Indonesia, in parts of Florida in the United States, and along parts of coastal Turkey and China. Saltwater intrusion is also a serious problem on islands such as the Maldives and Cyprus, which are very dependent on aquifers for water supply.[69]

Fluoride is another natural contaminant that threatens millions of people in parts of Asia. Aquifers in the drier regions of northwestern India, northern China, and parts of Thailand and Sri Lanka are naturally rich in fluoride deposits. Fluoride is an essential nutrient for bone and dental health, but when consumed in high concentrations, it can lead to crippling damage to the neck and back, and to a range of dental problems. WHO estimates that 70 million people in northern China, and 30 million in northwestern India are drinking water with excessive fluoride levels.[70]

Changing Course

The various incidents of aquifer pollution described thus far may seem isolated. A group of wells in northern China have nitrate problems; another lot in the United Kingdom are laced with solvents; yet another cluster in India have become too salty for human use. In each place it might seem that the problem is local and can be contained. But as you begin to step back, you see a bigger picture emerging. Some of the world's most populous and rapidly expanding regions are, in essence, unintentionally poisoning their own wells—thus giving up their supplies of a vital source of freshwater. Perhaps most worrisome is that scientists have discovered as much damage as they have, despite the very limited monitoring and testing of underground water. And because of the time-lags involved—and given our high levels of chemical use and waste generation in recent decades—the future is likely to bring even more unpleasant surprises.

In most cases, decisionmakers have responded to groundwater pollution largely with "end-of-pipe" solutions: utilities have installed filters, or engineers have tried to dilute the aquifer—and some communities have had to abandon their groundwater supplies altogether. Several towns and cities around the world have had to seek out alternate supplies of water because their groundwater has become unusable. (See Table 5.) In recent years, half of all wells in Santa Monica, California, for instance, have been shut down because of dangerously high levels of the gasoline additive MTBE.[71]

In places where alternate supplies aren't easily available, utilities will have to resort to increasingly elaborate filtration set-ups to make the water safe for drinking. In heavily contaminated areas, hundreds of different filters may be necessary. By one estimate, utilities in the U.S. Midwest spend an additional $400 million each year to treat water for just one chemical—atrazine, a commonly detected pesticide in U.S. groundwater. When chemicals are found in unpredictable mixtures, rather than discretely, providing safe water may become even more expensive.[72]

Where engineers have actually tried to "clean" contaminated aquifers, the favored technology has been "pump-and-treat." Three quarters of the highly contaminated Superfund sites in the United States where cleanup is under way use this technology. Groundwater is sucked out of the aquifer, its contaminants are flushed out or chemically treated above ground, and the water is injected back into the aquifer. This

TABLE 5

Aquifers Abandoned Due to Chemical Pollution, Selected Examples

Region	Chemical(s)	Comments
Bangkok, Thailand	Salt	Excessive pumping of groundwater caused seawater to enter the aquifer. Chloride levels increased 60-fold; many wells have been abandoned.
Santa Monica, California, United States	MTBE, a gasoline additive	A petroleum spill produced MTBE levels 30 times higher than the guideline. Wells supplying half the city's water had to be closed.
Shenyang, China	Nitrate, ammonium, oils, phenol, and other industrial pollutants	Overpumping and pollution have forced authorities to replace groundwater with more expensive surface water supplies.
Barceloneta, Puerto Rico	Carbon tetrachloride and other chlorinated solvents	A chemical spill from a storage tank at a pharmaceutical factory led to solvent levels as much as 100 times above guidelines. Costs of supplying alternate sources were $10 million.

Sources: See endnote 71.

technology works on the principle that decades of such treatment will ultimately dilute the underground contamination. But the amount of freshwater needed to purge an aquifer is "unimaginably large," say scientists at the U. S. National Research Council, adding that "simple calculations...show that predicted cleanup times range from a few years to tens, hundreds, and even thousands of years."[73]

The National Research Council estimates that in the

United States, the costs of cleaning up the known 300,000 to 400,000 heavily contaminated sites where groundwater is polluted will be as high as $1 trillion for the next 30 years alone. (So far, cleanup work has begun on just 4,000 of these sites since Superfund laws were passed in 1980.) Experts concur that in most cases, complete cleanup is near impossible. This is in large part due to the enormous size of aquifers and the persistent nature of many synthetic chemicals now found underground. Some of the radioactive waste that has leaked into Washington state's Central Columbia Plateau Aquifer has a half-life of 250,000 years. (Since 1943, hundreds of billions of gallons of radioactive wastes have been dumped into the aquifer and soils by the U.S. Department of Energy's Hanford Nuclear Reservation.) When such long-lived waste gets into aquifers—as it has in Washington—cleanup isn't even an option.[74]

In many places, various authorities and industries have tried to fight the contamination leak by leak, or chemical by chemical, only to find that the individual fixes simply don't add up. As we line landfills to reduce leakage, for instance, tons of pesticide may be running off nearby farms and into aquifers. As we mend holes in underground gas tanks, acid from mines may be seeping into groundwater. Clearly, it's essential to control the damage already inflicted, and to protect communities and ecosystems from the poisoned fallout. But given what we already know—that damage done to aquifers is mostly irreversible, that it can take years before groundwater pollution reveals itself, that chemicals react synergistically, and often in unanticipated ways—it is now clear that a patchwork response cannot be effective. (See Table 6.) Given how much damage this pollution inflicts on public health, the environment, and the economy once it gets into the water, it's critical that emphasis be shifted from filtering out toxins to not using them in the first place. Andrew Skinner, who heads the International Association of Hydrogeologists, puts it this way: "Prevention is the only credible strategy."[75]

Preventing groundwater pollution requires looking not

TABLE 6

Evaluating Responses to Groundwater Pollution

Strategy	Evaluation
End-of-pipe filters	Necessary if groundwater is the only available drinking water source. Expensive; does not protect people against multiple chemicals. Does not prevent pollution of aquifers.
Cleaning aquifers using "pump-and-treat" and other remediation technologies	Very expensive; can take decades or centuries before water quality improves significantly. Technically impossible to completely clean an aquifer. Does not prevent pollution of aquifers.
Restricting chemical use and disposal above vulnerable aquifers	Transfers polluting activity away from most vulnerable aquifers; does not prevent pollution from entering the environment altogether.
Changing polluting systems by moving toward closed-loop agricultural, urban, and industrial systems	Reduces the amount of pollution in the entire system, lightening the load on aquifers as well as other ecological systems.

Source: See endnote 75.

just at individual factories, gas stations, cornfields, and dry cleaning plants, but at the whole social, industrial, and agricultural systems of which these businesses are a part. It is these ecologically untenable systems that are poisoning the world's water. The predominant system of high-input agriculture, for example, not only shrinks biodiversity with its vast monocultures, but also overwhelms the land—and the underlying water—with its massive applications of agricultural chemicals. The system of car-dominated, geographically expanding cities not only generates unsustainable amounts of climate-disrupting greenhouse gases and acid rain-causing air pollutants, but also floods aquifers and soils with petrochemicals, heavy metals, and sewage. An adequate response will require a thoughtful overhaul of each of these systems.

Perhaps the most dramatic gains will come from retooling industrial agriculture to make it far less dependent on chemicals. Farm runoff is a leading cause of groundwater pollution in many parts of Europe, the United States, China, and India, and it is impossible to control this pollution in a piecemeal fashion. Lessening its impact thus calls for adopting practices that sharply reduce runoff—or, better still, that require far smaller amounts of fertilizers and pesticides to begin with. Even without major shifts in the way we farm, there is plenty of room to improve the efficiency of chemical use because in most places, current practices are excessively wasteful. On average, roughly 85–90 percent of pesticides used for agriculture never reach target organisms, but instead spread through the environment. In Brazil, for example, farmers spray orchards with as much as 10,000 liters of pesticide per hectare each week. Experts at FAO say that with modified application techniques, these chemicals could be applied at one tenth that amount and still be effective. Eliminating wasteful use is significant because it's typically the surplus that leaks into groundwater. In the Netherlands, some 550 farmers have reduced their levels of chemical inputs by between 30 and 50 percent—and have completely eliminated their insecticide use—by monitoring and altering their farming practices: testing soil fertility to estimate how much is needed in the way of additional nutrients, for example, and planting a diverse array of crops. Because the farmers have been able to maintain crop yields while using less input, their profit margins have increased. Meanwhile, their farms pollute far less: nitrogen and phosphorus levels in drainage water have declined 40–80 percent.[76]

But while greater efficiency constitutes a major improvement, more radical gains might be had by replacing chemicals with non-polluting methods to improve soil fertility and keep pests in check. Recent studies suggest that farms can still maintain high yields while using this approach. One decade-long investigation by the Rodale Institute in Pennsylvania, for example, compared traditional manure and legume-based cropping systems, which used no synthetic fertilizer or pesticides, with a conventional, high-intensity system. All three fields were planted with maize and soybeans. The researchers found that the two traditional systems retained more soil organic matter and nitrogen—indicators of soil fertility—and leached 60 percent less nitrate than the high-intensity system. Yields for the maize and soybean crops differed by less than 1 percent between the three cropping systems over the 10-year period.[77]

Nearly 150 years ago, Charles Darwin observed in *On the Origin of Species* that wheat fields planted in diverse varieties of the grain were more productive than those planted in single varieties. This is because mixtures check the spread of pathogens and therefore of disease. For centuries, farmers have practiced such "polycropping" to protect their fields against disease. In China, all the farmers in Yunnan Province recently confirmed Darwin's observations. Until 1998, the region's farmers planted monocultures of just two kinds of hybrid rice—and constantly battled the fungal disease rice blast with chemicals. But by growing multiple varieties of rice in the same paddies, they were able to double yields, and at the same time, to completely eliminate their use of fungicide.[78]

China's renewed success with polycropping could have profound implications for millions of farmers around the world. Single-species fields have become the norm in industrial countries only in the last 50 years, as average farm size has increased, and as operations have become more mechanized. As farms scale up, monocultures become simpler to manage than diverse fields, which require more labor and an intimate knowledge of local ecology. However, crop diversity provides an antidote to the inherent weaknesses of monocultures—the depletion of soil nutrients, for instance, and the vulnerability of such fields to pest infestations.[79]

Planting diverse species is one ecological method of pest control; other strategies include introducing a pest's natural predators, for instance, or interspersing crops with plants that repel pests. "Integrated Pest Management," or IPM, incorporates several such ecological tools, using chemical pesticide only as a last resort. In 1986, after losing $1 billion worth of its rice crop to an insect called the brown plant-hopper, Indonesia adopted IPM as a national pest control strategy. Originally a secondary pest, the planthopper had upended the country's progress toward a goal of self-sufficiency in rice production after its predators were decimated by pesticides. The failure of chemicals to control pests prompted the government to look for an alternate solution. Hundreds of thousands of farmers were taught IPM strategies in "Farmer Field Schools"—and their training brought impressive results. In the first 4 years of the program, pesticide use on rice fell by half, and at the same time, yields increased by 15 percent.[80]

Similar IPM programs have helped rice farmers in seven other Asian countries to cut pesticide use nearly by half, while raising yields on average 10 percent. Despite the efforts of some researchers and pesticide companies who have promoted a watered down version of the program—suggesting that farmers might rotate pesticides, for instance, rather than phase out their use—truly ecological IPM of the kind practiced in Indonesia has proven itself in several parts of the world, including Kenya, Cuba, Peru, and Iowa in the United States.[81]

Reining in agriculture's excessive dependence on chemicals will call for innovative responses not just from farmers, but from policymakers and businesses too. For instance, Indonesia's success is owed in large part to parallel changes in policies: 57 pesticides were banned for use on rice, and pesticide subsidies were removed, saving the government $120 million. Several European countries including Denmark, Finland, Norway, and Sweden now tax pesticide sales to encourage farmers to use smaller quantities of chemicals. Sweden's 7.5 percent tax (per kilogram of active ingredient) has had impressive results: it helped slash the country's pesticide use by 65 percent between 1986 and 1993. The program is still under way, with the goal of reducing pesticide use by another half. The French government is considering a steep tax on fertilizers and pesticides, spurred largely by water pollution problems in the country.[82]

In Germany, private water supply companies have discovered the economic benefits of organic farming. Firms in Munich, Osnabrück, and Leipzig pay local farmers as much as 550 Deutsche marks per hectare for three years to convert to organic operations. The firms are responsible for supplying clean water to their customers, and have found that it costs less to invest in sustainable farming than to strip pesticides out of polluted water.[83]

New York City has also worked with farmers to protect its water sources. The city's water supply depends on 5,000 square kilometers of watershed located 250 kilometers to its north. The watershed is also home to many of New York's small dairy farmers, who grow corn and hay for feed. Policymakers in the 1980s knew that farm runoff would affect water quality, but believed that the only way to protect New York's water supply was by installing elaborate filtration systems. The filters would have doubled the costs of the city's water, and mandatory farm regulations would have put many small farmers out of business.[84]

EPA estimates that reducing agricultural pollution could save at least $15 billion...

Concerned about the expense and shortsightedness of this solution, Al Appleton, the Commissioner of the city's Department of Environmental Protection, began to develop an alternate plan in 1991. Today, the farmer-led Watershed Agricultural Council helps New York's farmers better manage their operations to protect water quality—for example, to time their fertilizer applications better, and to be more efficient with their use of chemicals. Although it is too early to quantify the water quality benefits, the program's financial savings have been considerable. While the filtration system would have cost upwards of $4 billion, New York City's watershed protection will cost an estimated $1.5 billion. Nationwide, EPA estimates that reducing agricultural pollution could save at least $15 billion in avoided costs of constructing advanced water treatment facilities.[85]

In industrial settings, building "closed-loop" production and consumption systems can help slash the amounts of waste that factories and cities send to landfills, sewers, and dumps—and thus protect aquifers from leaking pollutants. In places as far-ranging as Fiji, Namibia, Denmark, and Tennessee in the United States, environmentally conscious investors have begun to build "industrial symbiosis" parks in which the unusable wastes from one firm become the input for another. Such waste exchanges help an industrial park in Kalundborg, Denmark, to keep more than 1.3 million tons of effluent out of landfills and septic systems each year, while preventing some 135,000 tons of carbon and sulfur from leaking into the atmosphere. By reusing spent materials and chemicals, individuals and firms can help reduce the risk of groundwater pollution from heavy metals, insulation chemicals, cleaning solvents, and other toxic substances that leak out of landfills. The Xerox Corporation, for example, remanufactures more than a third of all its photocopiers by using components from older machines—a strategy that saved 143,000 tons of materials from being dumped in landfills in 1999 alone. Each remanufactured machine must meet the same standards and comes with the same warranty as a newly minted one.[86]

Xerox also reports that since 1991 it has nearly halved it use of dichloromethane, a solvent used to make photoreceptors. Currently, the firm reuses or recycles 97 percent of the solvent, and ultimately intends to replace the chemical with a non-toxic alternative. In the last decade, substitutes for petrochemical-based solvents have begun to make inroads for many uses, including industrial cleaning, degreasing, and stripping paints. Many of these alternatives are water-based, and derived from biochemical sources such as citrus fruits, corn, soybean, or lactic acid. In Sweden, where chlorinated solvents are being entirely phased out by the end of 2000, some firms already report economic savings from making the switch.[87]

Some regions have set waste reduction as a collective goal. The Netherlands, for instance, has a national goal of cutting its wastes 70–90 percent. Pollution taxes have already helped the Netherlands slash discharges of heavy metals such as mercury and arsenic into waterways by 72–99 percent between 1976 and the mid-1990s. The city of Canberra in Australia aims for a "No-Waste-by-2010" goal. As part of the campaign, authorities in the city have set up an online resource exchange—an information center that helps to match suppliers of waste material with buyers.[88]

Scientists believe that a large part of the resource still remains pure—for the moment.

In some cases, the costs of using a particular chemical are so great that the only way to protect human health and the environment adequately may be to eliminate its use completely. In 1987, for instance, the global community signed a treaty phasing out the use of substances that were found to deplete the ozone layer. Since that time, their use has fallen substantially—by 88 percent in the case of chlorofluorocarbons, chemicals that were commonplace in refrigerators and air conditioners just a few years earlier. Currently under negotiation is an international treaty on a class of dangerous synthetic materials known as "persistent organic pollutants." Negotiators are discussing a proposed phaseout of 12 chemicals nicknamed "The Dirty Dozen"—9 of which are pesticides, including DDT and dieldrin. Many participants in the treaty process argue that the list of chemicals to be phased out should be expanded to include dozens, even hundreds, of other persistent chemicals whose presence in the environment poses an unacceptable risk to humanity.[89]

As it becomes clearer to decisionmakers that the most serious threats to human security are no longer those of military attack but of pervasive environmental and social decline, experts worry about the difficulty of mustering suf-

ficient political will to bring about the kinds of systemic—
and therefore revolutionary—changes in human life necessary to turn the tide in time. In confronting the now heavily
documented assaults of climate change and biodiversity loss,
leaders seem paralyzed by the apparent bleakness of the big
picture on the one hand, and the seeming lack of immediate
consequences of delay on the other.

But the need to protect aquifers may provide a more
immediate incentive for change. It simply may not be possible to live with contaminated groundwater for as long as we
could make do with a gradually more irritable climate or polluted air or impoverished wildlife. Although we've damaged
portions of some aquifers to the point of no return, scientists
believe that a large part of the resource still remains pure—
for the moment. That is unlikely to remain the case if we
continue to depend on simply stepping up the present reac-
tive tactics of cleaning up more chemical spills, replacing
more leaking gasoline tanks, putting more plastic liners
under landfills, or issuing more fines to careless hog farms
and copper mines. Protecting our water in time requires the
same fundamental restructuring of the global economy as
does the stabilizing of the climate and biosphere as a whole—
the transition from a resource-depleting, oil- and coal-fueled,
high-input industrial and agricultural economy to one that is
based on renewable energy, compact cities, and a light
human footprint. We have been slow to come to grips with
this imperative, but our thirst may finally force us to act.

Notes

1.   Francis H. Chapelle, *The Hidden Sea: Ground Water, Springs, and Wells* (Tucson, AZ: Geoscience Press, Inc., 1997), 116–18.

2.   U.N. Environment Programme (UNEP), *Groundwater: A Threatened Resource* (Nairobi: 1996), 4.

3.   Groundwater recycling time and 30 millennia from UNEP, op. cit. note 2, 6–7; rivers from Igor A. Shiklomanov, *World Water Resources: A New Appraisal and Assessment for the 21st Century* (Paris: International Hydrological Programme, United Nations Educational, Scientific and Cultural Organization, 1998), 6.

4.   Production from Anne Platt McGinn, "Phasing Out Persistent Organic Pollutants," in Lester Brown et al., *State of the World 2000* (New York: W.W. Norton & Company, 2000), 81; toxicity from D. Pimentel and D. Kahn, "Environmental Aspects of 'Cosmetic Standards' of Foods and Pesticides," in David Pimentel, ed., *Techniques for Reducing Pesticide Use: Economic and Environmental Benefits* (New York: John Wiley & Sons, 1997), 415.

5.   P.J. Chilton, A.R. Lawrence, and M.E. Stuart, "Pesticides in Groundwater: Some Preliminary Results From Recent Research in Temperate and Tropical Environments," in J. Mather et al., eds., *Groundwater Contaminants and Their Migration* (London: Geological Society, 1998), 335.

6.   Sandra Postel, *Pillar of Sand* (New York: W.W. Norton & Company, 1999), 59; National Research Council (NRC), *Alternatives for Ground Water Cleanup* (Washington, DC: National Academy Press, 1994), viii; Janet Raloff, "Hanford Tanks: Leaks Reach Groundwater," *Science News*, 20 December 1997, 410.

7.   Postel, op. cit. note 6, 80; overdraft and pollution from Stephen Foster, Adrian Lawrence, and Brian Morris, *Groundwater in Urban Development*, World Bank Technical Paper 390 (Washington, DC: World Bank, 1998) 6, 23–25.

8.   Peter H. Gleick, *The World's Water 2000–2001: The Biennial Report on Freshwater Resources* (Washington, DC: Island Press, 2000), 165–66, 170.

9. $1 trillion from NRC, op. cit. note 6, 1; fertilizer from NRC, *Soil and Water Quality: An Agenda for Agriculture* (Washington, DC: National Academy Press, 1993); pesticides from Robert Repetto and Sanjay S. Baliga, *Pesticides and the Immune System: The Public Health Risks* (Washington, DC: World Resources Institute (WRI), 1996), 13.

10.   China from Youyung Zhu et al., "Genetic Diversity and Disease Control in Rice," *Nature*, vol. 406, 17 August 2000, 718–21; Indonesia and other countries from Lori Ann Thrupp, ed., *New Partnerships For Sustainable Agriculture* (Washington, DC: WRI, 1996), 6–9; Gary Gardner, "IPM and the

War on Pests," *World Watch*, March/April 1996, 26.

11. Hydrological cycle from Ralph Heath, *Basic Ground-Water Hydrology*, United States Geological Survey (USGS) Water-Supply Paper 2220 (Washington, DC: U.S. Government Printing Office, 1998), 5; Broecker quoted in William K. Stevens, "If Climate Changes, It May Change Quickly," *New York Times*, 27 January 1998.

12. Water witches from Chapelle, op. cit. note 1, 43.

13. Table 1 and drinking water figure based on United States Environmental Protection Agency (EPA), Office of Water, *The Quality of Our Nation's Water* (Washington, DC: 1998), on Environment Australia, *State of the Environment Report 1996* (Canberra: 1996), on Asia-Pacific and Latin America data from UNEP, op. cit. note 2, 10–11, and on European data from Organisation for Economic Co-operation and Development, *Water Resources Management: Integrated Policies* (Paris: 1989); Eastern China and urban dependence from UNEP, op. cit. note 2, 8, 10; EPA, Office of Water, *National Water Quality Inventory: 1998 Report to Congress* (Washington, DC: 2000), 158, at <www.epa.gov/305b/98Report>, viewed 30 June 2000; India from Stephen Foster, et al., *Groundwater in Rural Development: Facing the Challenges of Supply and Resource Sustainability*, World Bank Technical Paper No. 463 (Washington, DC: World Bank, 2000), 2.

14. Tubewells from Tata Energy Research Institute (TERI), *Looking Back to Think Ahead: GREEN India 2047*, abridged text (New Delhi: 1998), 12; agricultural product and GDP from World Bank and Ministry of Water Resources, Government of India, *Groundwater Regulation and Management*, South Asia Rural Development Series (New Delhi: World Bank and Allied Publishers, 1999), 2; U.S. irrigated area today and current contribution of freshwater to irrigation from Postel, op. cit. note 6, 42, 112; current irrigation by aquifers from data supplied by Charlotte De Fraiture, International Water Management Institute (IWMI), e-mail to author, 21 October 1999.

15. Industry to agriculture ratio from Lester R. Brown and Brian Halweil, "China's Water Shortage Could Shake World Food Security," *World Watch*, July/August 1998, 13; industrial share of consumption from Sandra Postel, *Dividing the Waters: Food Security, Ecosystem Health, and the New Politics of Scarcity*, Worldwatch Paper 132 (Washington, DC: Worldwatch Institute, September 1996), 14.

16. Shiang-Kueen Hsu, "Plan for a Groundwater Monitoring Network in Taiwan," *Hydrogeology Journal*, vol. 6 (1998), 407; Bangladesh from Gleick, op. cit. note 8, 165–66; International Bottled Water Association, Alexandria, VA, *Bottled Water in the U.S.*, 1999 Edition, <www.bottledwater.org/public/gallon_byseg.htm>, viewed 5 April 2000.

17. Postel, op. cit. note 6, 80.

18. California from Postel, op. cit. note 15, 19; subsidence from UNEP, op. cit. note 2, 17–18.

19. USGS, *Ground Water and Surface Water: A Single Resource*, USGS Circular 1139 (Denver, CO: 1998), 12; daily addition from aquifers from EPA, *The Quality of Our Nation's Water*, op. cit. note 13; the contribution to major rivers from Francis Chapelle, hydrologist, USGS, Columbia, SC, discussion with author, 5 November 1999.

20. USGS, *Ground Water and Surface Water*, op. cit. note 19, 19; Azraq from Tushaar Shah et al., *The Global Groundwater Situation: Overview of Opportunities and Challenges* (Colombo: IWMI, 2000), 3.

21. UNEP, op. cit. note 2, 12–13; Africa from Shiklomanov, op. cit. note 3, 25.

22. Chapelle, op. cit. note 1, 167–80.

23. Ibid.

24. Ibid.

25. Table 2 compiled from various sources cited in this Paper.

26. Jack E. Barbash, Research Chemist, USGS, Tacoma, WA, discussion with author, 17 November 1999.

27. Barbara K. Rhodes and Rice O'Dell, eds., *A Dictionary of Environmental Quotations* (Baltimore: Johns Hopkins University Press, 1992), 59.

28. U.N. Food and Agriculture Organization (FAO), *Fertilizers: A World Report on Production and Consumption* (Rome: 1952), 3; FAO, *Agriculture, Means of Production, Fertilizer*, electronic database, <apps.fao.org>, accessed 10 April 2000; W.L. Zhang et al., "Nitrate Pollution of Groundwater in Northern China," *Agriculture, Ecosystems and Environment*, vol. 59 (1996), 223–31; NRC, op. cit. note 9; Paul Faeth, *Fertile Ground* (Washington, DC: WRI, 2000), 7, 16.

29. Figure of 130 times from Faeth, op. cit. note 28, 11; Brian Halweil, "United States Leads World Meat Stampede," press briefing (Washington, DC: Worldwatch Institute, 2 July 1998).

30. WHO limit from UNEP, op. cit. note 2, 22. The drinking water limit is 10 mg/liter of nitrogen which is equivalent to 45 mg/liter of nitrate. China from Zhang et al., op. cit. note 28, 223–31.

31. Text examples and Table 3 from the following: Zhang et al., op. cit. note 28, 223–31; Geoffrey D. Smith et al., "The Origin and Distribution of Nitrate in Groundwater from Village Wells in Kotagede, Yogyakarta, Indonesia," *Hydrogeology Journal*, vol. 7 (1999), 576–89; Canary Islands and

East Anglia from Gordon Conway and Jules Pretty, *Unwelcome Harvest* (London: Earthscan Publications, 1991), 183–84, 196; Nigeria from Foster et al., op. cit. note 13, 84; Romania and Moldova from European Environmental Agency (EEA), *Groundwater Quality and Quantity in Europe* (Copenhagen: 1999), 53–60; Julia A. Pacheco and Armando S. Cabrera, "Groundwater Contamination by Nitrates in the Yucatan Peninsula, Mexico," *Hydrogeology Journal*, vol. 5, no. 2 (1997), 47; and Nebraska and Kansas from David K. Mueller et al., *Nutrients in Ground Water and Surface Water of the United States—An Analysis of Data through 1992* (Denver, CO: USGS, National Water Quality Assessment Program, 1995), 35. Levels for Nebraska and Kansas converted by author from nitrogen to nitrate equivalent. India from TERI, op. cit. note 14, unabridged version, 215; United States from USGS, *The Quality of Our Nation's Waters—Nutrients and Pesticides* (Reston, VA: 1999); Sri Lanka from UNEP, op. cit. note 2, 29.

32. San Joaquin from USGS, op. cit. note 31, 54; Denmark from Larry W. Canter, *Nitrates in Groundwater* (New York: Lewis Publishers, 1997), 58–59; Linda Nash, "Water Quality and Health," in Peter H. Gleick, ed., *Water in Crisis* (New York: Oxford University Press, 1993), 28.

33. Nash, op. cit. note 32, 27–28; Joseph I. Barzilay, Winkler G. Weinberg, and J. William Eley, *The Water We Drink* (New Brunswick, NJ: Rutgers University Press, 1999), 70–71; links to miscarriages and lymphoma from Bernard T. Nolan and Jeffrey D. Stoner, "Nutrients in Groundwaters of the Conterminous United States, 1992–1995," *Environmental Science & Technology*, vol. 34, no. 7 (2000), 1156; Ruminant animals from EEA, op. cit. note 31, 51.

34. Grapevines, overall effects of nitrates, and FAO from R.S. Ayers and D.W. Westcott, *Water Quality for Agriculture*, FAO Irrigation and Drainage Paper 29 (Rome: FAO, 1985), 91; other effects from George N. Agrios, *Plant Pathology*, 4th Edition (San Diego, CA: Academic Press, 1997), 149–50, and from Ian McPharlin, *Nitrogen and Phosphorous Disorders of Vegetable Crops*, Bulletin No. 4175 (South Perth, Australia: Western Australian Department of Agriculture, December 1989), 6.

35. Scott Phillips, Michael Focazio, and L. Joseph Bachman, *Discharge, Nitrate Load, and Residence Time of Ground Water in the Chesapeake Bay Watershed* (Baltimore, MD: USGS, 1998); USGS, "The Bay's Recovery: How Long Will it Take?" (Baltimore, MD: April 1998).

36. Groundwater contribution to Chesapeake Bay from Phillips, Focazio, and Bachman, op. cit. note 35; USGS, op. cit. note 35; Lake Mendota from U.S. Congress, Office of Technology Assessment (OTA), *Beneath the Bottom Line: Agricultural Approaches to Reduce Agrichemical Contamination of Groundwater* (Washington, DC: GPO, November 1990), 34.

37. Nolan and Stoner, op. cit. note 33, 1163–64 (examples include the White River Basin in southern Indiana and parts of the Western Michigan

Drainages); Mueller et al., op. cit. note 31, 38.

38. Mueller et al., op. cit. note 31, 1, 38.

39. Conway and Pretty, op. cit. note 31, 194; EEA, op. cit. note 31, 21.

40. Soil as filter from EPA, *The Quality of Our Nation's Water*, op. cit. note 13; Foster et al., op. cit. note 13, 77.

41. USGS, op. cit. note 31, 58; Jack E. Barbash and Elizabeth A. Resek, *Pesticides in Ground Water: Distribution, Trends, and Governing Factors* (Chelsea, MI: Ann Arbor Press, 1996), 115–17.

42. DDT from Barbash and Resek, op. cit. note 41, 141; DBCP from Joseph L. Domagalski, *Pesticides in Surface and Ground Water of the San Joaquin-Tulare Basins, California: Analysis of Available data, 1966 through 1992* (Washington, DC: USGS, 1997), 42–47; dieldrin from USGS, op. cit. note 31, 74.

43. TERI, op. cit. note 14, unabridged version, 216.

44. Chilton, Lawrence, and Stuart, op. cit. note 5, 335.

45. Nash, op. cit. note 32, 31–32; Polly Short and Theo Colburn, "Pesticide Use in the U.S. and Policy Implications: A Focus on Herbicides," *Toxicology and Industrial Health*, vol. 15, nos. 1–2 (1999), 240–43; Repetto and Baliga, op. cit. note 9; Ted Schettler, Gina Solomon, Maria Valenti, and Annette Huddle, *Generations at Risk: Reproductive Health and the Environment* (Cambridge, MA: The MIT Press, 1999), 107.

46. Table 4 from the following sources: Nolan and Stoner, op. cit. note 33, 1156; USGS, op. cit. note 31, 57–58, 76; and Paul J. Squillace et al., "Volatile Organic Compounds in Untreated Ambient Groundwater of the United States," *Environmental Science & Technology*, vol. 33, no. 23 (1999), 4176; herbicide degradates and Figure 1 from Jack E. Barbash et al., *Distribution of Major Herbicides in Ground Water of the United States* (Sacramento, CA: USGS, 1999), 1, 25, 27; degradate toxicity from Conway and Pretty, op. cit. note 31, 40.

47. EPA, Office of Water, "Current Drinking Water Standards," (Washington, DC: 1995), at <www.epa.gov/safewater/mcl.html>, viewed 7 August 2000; Warren P. Porter, James W. Jaeger, and Ian H. Carlson, "Endocrine, Immune, and Behavioral Effects of Aldicarb (Carbamate), Atrazine (Triazine) and Nitrate (Fertilizer) Mixtures at Groundwater Concentrations," *Toxicology and Industrial Health*, vol. 15, nos. 1–2 (1999), 135, 142–43.

48. OTA, op. cit. note 36, 34.

49. Barbash and Resek, op. cit. note 41, 285, 289.

50. Brian Halweil, "Pesticide-Resistant Species Flourish," in Lester R. Brown, Michael Renner, and Brian Halweil, *Vital Signs 1999* (New York: W.W. Norton & Company, 1999), 125–26.

51. Chilton, Lawrence, and Stuart, op. cit. note 5, 336–37.

52. Aaron Sachs, "Virtual Ecology: A Brief Environmental History of Silicon Valley," *World Watch*, January/February 1999, 13; EPA, *Safe Drinking Water Act, Section 1429 Ground Water Report to Congress* (Washington, DC: 1999), 16.

53. EPA, *The Quality of Our Nation's Water*, op. cit. note 13; U.K. from "Aquifer Pollution Inventory Sets the Scene for Tussles over Clean-Up," *ENDS Report*, September 1996, 17.

54. David A. Bender et al., *Selection Procedure and Salient Information for Volatile Organic Compounds Emphasized in the National Water-Quality Assessment Program* (Rapid City, SD: USGS, 1999), 1; "42 Million Americans Use Groundwater Vulnerable to Contamination by Volatile Organic Compounds," *ScienceDaily Magazine*, 29 October 1999 at <www.science daily.com>.

55. Uses from Bender et al., op. cit. note 54, 1, and from Squillace et al., op. cit. note 46, 4176–87.

56. James F. Pankow and John A. Cherry, *Dense Chlorinated Solvents and other DNAPLs in Groundwater* (Waterloo, ON, Canada: Waterloo Press, 1996), 7–15; UNEP, op. cit. note 2, 26.

57. Schettler et al., op. cit. note 45; 73, 77, 82; kidney and liver damage and childhood cancers from Pankow and Cherry, op. cit. note 56.

58. Pankow and Cherry, op. cit. note 56, 9; EPA, *The Quality of Our Nation's Water*, op. cit. note 13.

59. Donald Sutherland, "60 Percent of America's Liquid Toxic Waste Injected Underground," *Environment News Service*, <www.ens-news.com>, 7 July 1999; EPA, "Class I Injection Wells Underground Injection Control Regulations for Florida; Proposed Rule," draft (Tallahassee, FL: 24 April 2000) provided by Suzi Ruhl, Legal Environmental Assistance Foundation, Inc., Tallahassee, FL; India from Manish Tiwari and Richard Mahapatra, "What Goes Down Must Come Up," *Down to Earth*, 31 August 1999, 30–40.

60. Squillace, et al., op. cit. note 46, 4176–87; Squillace quoted in "42 Million Americans," op. cit. note 54.

61. Netherlands from European Centre for Ecotoxicology and Toxicology of Chemicals, *Joint Assessment of Commodity Chemicals No. 39—Tetrachloro-ethylene CAS No. 127-18-4* (Brussels: 1999), 42; England from "Aquifer Pollution Inventory," op. cit. note 53, 15; Japan from British Geological

Survey (BGS) et al., *Characterisation and Assessment of Groundwater Quality Concerns in Asia-Pacific Region* (Oxfordshire, U.K.: 1996), 49–51; semiconductors from Semiconductor Industry Association, *Semiconductor Forecast Summary, 2000–2003* (San Jose, CA, June 2000).

62. Biswas quoted in Tiwari and Mahapatra, op. cit. note 59, 39.

63. UNEP, op. cit. note 2, 14.

64. Arnab Neil Sengupta, "Bangladesh Arsenic an Invitation to Catastrophe," *Environmental News Network*, 23 March 1998, at <www.enn. com>; World Health Organization (WHO), "Arsenic in Drinking Water," Fact Sheet No. 210 (Geneva: February 1999), 4.

65. Numbers of people affected from BGS and Mott MacDonald (U.K.), "Phase I, Groundwater Studies of Arsenic Contamination in Bangladesh," Executive Summary, Main Report, <bicn.com/acic/infobank/bgs-mmi/ risumm.htm>, viewed 9 July 1999; Uttam K. Chowdhury et al., "Groundwater Arsenic Contamination in Bangladesh and West Bengal, India," *Environmental Health Perspectives*, May 2000, 393–94; Nadia S. Halim, "Arsenic Mitigation in Bangladesh," *The Scientist*, 6 March 2000, 14; Sengupta, op. cit. note 64, 3. The BGS reports that 20 million Bangladeshis may be drinking arsenic contaminated water; estimates from scientists and medical workers in Bangladesh are considerably higher, on the order of 70–75 million. Number of wells affected from Ross Nickson et al., "Arsenic Poisoning of Bangladesh Groundwater," *Nature*, 24 September 1998, 338; deaths from Kimberley Masibay, "Drinking Without Harm," *Scientific American*, September 2000, 22; WHO prediction from Chowdhury et al., op. cit. this note, 393.

66. Helen Sewell, "Poison Threat in Bangladesh," *BBC News Online*, 6 October 1999, <www.bbc.co.uk/hi>; Sengupta, op. cit. note 64, 1; Gleick, op. cit. note 8, 165–67.

67. Scientists debate from Nickson et al., op. cit. note 65, 338; Gleick, op. cit. note 8, 171–72; S.K. Acharyya et al., "Arsenic Poisoning in the Ganges Delta," *Nature*, 7 October 1999, 545.

68. Two percent from EEA, op. cit. note 31, 91; abandoned aquifers from BGS et al., op. cit. note 61, 19–20; Shah et al., op. cit. note 20, 6–7.

69. UNEP, op. cit. note 2, 18–19; Turkey and China from Shah et al., op. cit. note 20, 6.

70. WHO in BGS et al., op. cit. note 61, 86–88.

71. Table 5 from the following sources: Bangkok and China from BGS et al., op. cit. note 61, 19–20, 3; China from Foster, Lawrence, and Morris, op. cit. note 7, 25; Santa Monica from Richard Johnson et al., "MTBE: To What Extent Will Past Releases Contaminate Community Water Supply Wells?"

Environmental Science & Technology, 1 May 2000, 2A; Puerto Rico from Stephen Foster, Miguel Ventura, and Ricardo Hirata, *Groundwater Pollution: An Executive Overview of the Latin American-Caribbean Situation in Relation to Potable Water-Supply* (Lima: WHO and Pan American Health Organization, 1987), 30, and UNEP, op. cit. note 2, 27.

72. U.S. utilities from Marc O. Ribaudo and Aziz Bouzaher, *Atrazine: Environmental Characteristics and Economics of Management*, Agricultural Economic Report No. 699 (Washington, DC: U.S. Department of Agriculture, September 1994), 5.

73. NRC, op. cit. note 6, viii, 1–6.

74. Ibid., 1; Raloff, op. cit. note 6, 410.

75. Table 6 from NRC, op. cit. note 6, and UNEP, op. cit. note 2; quote from Andrew Skinner, Secretary, International Association of Hydrogeologists, London, e-mail to author, 18 November 1999.

76. T.J. Logan, "Sustainable Agriculture and Water Quality," in Clive A. Edwards et al., *Sustainable Agricultural Systems* (Ankeny, IA: Soil and Water Conservation Society, 1990), 582–608; 85–90 percent from Repetto and Baliga, op. cit. note 9; 13; FAO, "FAO: Unsafe Application of Pesticides Causes Health and Environmental Damage—Training and Standards Required," press release (Rome: 29 May 1997); Netherlands from Jules Pretty, *The Living Land: Agriculture, Food and Community Regeneration in Rural Europe* (London: Earthscan Publications Ltd., 1998), 101.

77. L.E. Drinkwater, P. Wagoner, and M. Sarrantonio, "Legume-based Cropping Systems Have Reduced Carbon and Nitrogen Losses," *Nature*, 19 November 1999, 262–65; David Tilman, "The Greening of the Green Revolution," *Nature*, 19 November 1998, 211; Cass Petersen, Laurie E. Drinkwater, and Peggy Wagoner, *The Rodale Institute Farming Systems Trials* (Kutztown, PA: Rodale Institute, 1999).

78. Charles Darwin, *On the Origin of Species by Means of Natural Selection* (New York: Modern Library, 1993); Martin S. Wolfe, "Crop Strength Through Diversity," *Nature*, vol. 406, 17 August 2000, 681–82; Zhu et al., op. cit. note 10, 718–21.

79. Brian Halweil, "Where Have All the Farmers Gone?" *World Watch*, September/October 2000, 24–25.

80. Thrupp, op. cit. note 10, 6–9; Gardner, op. cit. note 10, 26.

81. Thrupp, op. cit. note 10, 6–9; Gardner, op. cit. note 10, 26.

82. Indonesia from Gardner, op. cit. note 10; Europe from Pretty, op. cit. note 76, 279–80; Sweden from Anders Emmerman, "Sweden's Reduced Risk

Pesticide Policy," *Pesticides News*, December 1996; and Short and Colburn, op. cit. note 45, 247; "Report Implicates Agriculture for Damage to the Environment, Recommends Eco-Taxes," *International Environment Reporter*, 17 March 1999; "Voynet Unveils Water Policy Reform With Extended 'Polluter Pays' Provisions," *International Environment Reporter*, 10 November 1999.

83. Pretty, op. cit. note 76, 283–84.

84. WRI et al., *World Resources 2000–01* (New York: Oxford University Press, 2000), 210–11; Watershed Agricultural Council, "Whole Farm Planning," Summary Report (New York: January 1996), 2–3.

85. WRI et al., op. cit. note 84, 210–11; Al Appleton, former Director of the New York City Water and Sewer System, e-mail to Danielle Nierenberg, Worldwatch Institute, 2 August 2000; Jeffrey Gatz, EPA Region II NYC Watershed Team Leader, e-mail to Danielle Nierenberg, Worldwatch Institute, 4 August 2000; EPA from Faeth, op. cit. note 28, 16.

86. John Ehrenfeld and Nicholas Gertler, "Industrial Ecology in Practice: The Evolution of Interdependence at Kalundborg," *Journal of Industrial Ecology*, vol. 1, no. 1 (1997); Braden R. Allenby, *Industrial Ecology: Framework and Implementation* (Upper Saddle River, NJ: Prentice Hall, 1999); Xerox website, <www.xerox.com/ehs/1997/sustain.htm>, viewed 18 September 1998; Xerox Corporation, *Environment, Health and Safety 2000 Progress Report* (Stamford, CT: 2000), 8; Liz Campbell, Regulatory Affairs Manager, Environment, Health and Safety Office, Xerox Corporation, Webster, New York, discussion with author, 2 November 2000.

87. Xerox Corporation, *Progress Report*, op. cit. note 86; 19; Julie Sherman et al., "Solvent Replacement for Green Processing," *Environmental Health Perspectives*, February 1998, vol. 106, supplement 1, 253–67; Institute for Local Self-Reliance (ILSR), *Biochemicals for the Automotive Industry* (Minneapolis, MN: 1997); ILSR, "Biochemical Cleaning Solvents," factsheet, 1996, available at <www.carbohydrateeconomy.org>; Schettler et al., op. cit. note 45, 384–85.

88. Netherlands goal from <www.netherlands-embassy.org/env_nmp2. htm>, viewed 20 August 1998; pollution taxes from David Roodman, *The Natural Wealth of Nations* (New York: W.W. Norton & Company, 1998), 151–52; Canberra from ACT government, <www.act.gov.au/nowaste/>, viewed 23 October 1998.

89. Chlorofluorocarbons from Molly O'Meara, "CFC Production Continues to Plummet," in Lester Brown, Michael Renner, and Christopher Flavin, *Vital Signs 1998* (New York: W.W. Norton & Company, 1998), 70–71; UNEP, "Regional Workshops Highlight Need for Effective Action Against Hazardous Chemicals," press release (Geneva: 9 July 1998); Anne Platt McGinn, *Why Poison Ourselves? A Precautionary Approach to Synthetic Chemicals*, Worldwatch Paper 153 (Washington, DC: Worldwatch Institute, November 2000), 7–8.

Worldwatch Online

www.worldwatch.org

Additional copies of *Deep Trouble: The Hidden Threat of Groundwater Pollution* and many other Worldwatch publications can be downloaded as PDF files from our website at **www.worldwatch.org**. Save time and shipping costs by ordering online.

Save even more by subscribing to the **State of the World Library**! Receive *State of the World* and all the highly readable, up-to-date, and authoritative Worldwatch Papers as they are released during the calendar year. Purchased separately, *State of the World* and the Worldwatch Papers cost $41, plus postage. For just $30 (international subscribers $45), you can be among the first to receive the book and Papers, *and* save $11.

Orders for printed publications, including subscriptions, can also be placed through our website.

For more information about Worldwatch Institute, please visit our website at **www.worldwatch.org**, or contact us at the address below:

Worldwatch Institute
1776 Massachusetts Ave., NW
Washington, DC 20036-1904 USA
phone: (800) 555-2028 or (301) 567-9522
fax: (301) 567-9553
e-mail: wwpub@worldwatch.org
website: www.worldwatch.org

Wish to make a tax-deductible contribution? Contact Worldwatch to find out how your donation can help advance our work.

WORLDWATCH INSTITUTE
1776 Massachusetts Ave., NW
Washington, DC 20036
www.worldwatch.org